IRON MAN

IRON ARMORY

IRON MAN

IRON ARMORY

WRITER: Fred Van Lente
PENCILERS: Rafa Sandoval, James Cordeiro
& Graham Nolan
INKERS: Roger Bonet, Gary Erskine
& Victor Olazaba
COLORISTS: Martegod Gracia & Ulises Arreola
LETTERER: Dave Sharpe

COVER ARTIST: Skottie Young

ASSISTANT EDITOR: Nathan Cosby
EDITOR: Mark Paniccia

COLLECTION EDITOR: Jennifer Grünwald
ASSISTANT EDITORS: Cory Levine & John Denning
EDITOR, SPECIAL PROJECTS: Mark D. Beazley
SENIOR EDITOR, SPECIAL PROJECTS: Jeff Youngquist
SENIOR VICE PRESIDENT OF SALES: David Gabriel
PRODUCTION: Jerry Kalinowski & Jerron Quality Color
VICE PRESIDENT OF CREATIVE: Tom Marvelli

EDITOR IN CHIEF: Joe Quesada
PUBLISHER: Dan Buckley

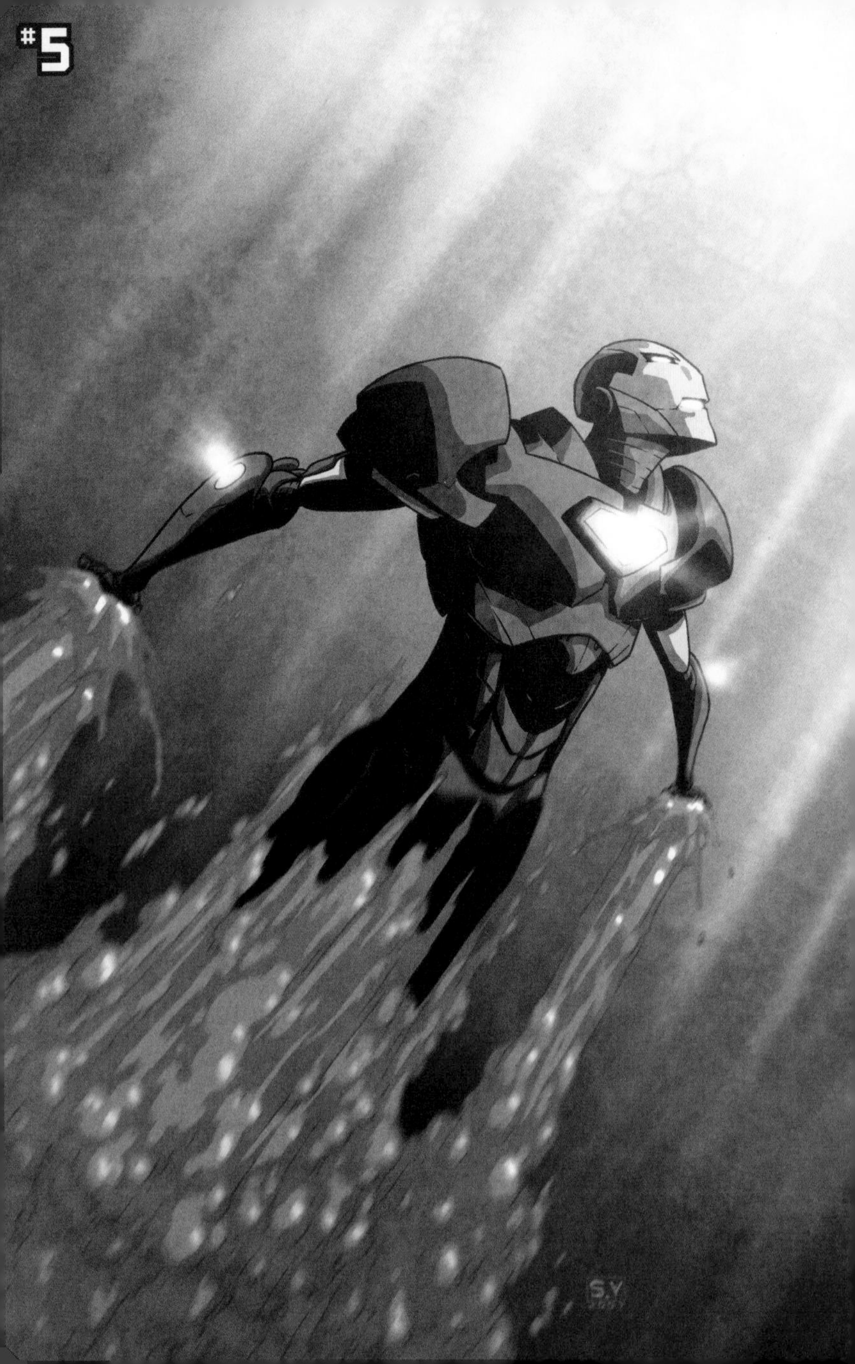
#5

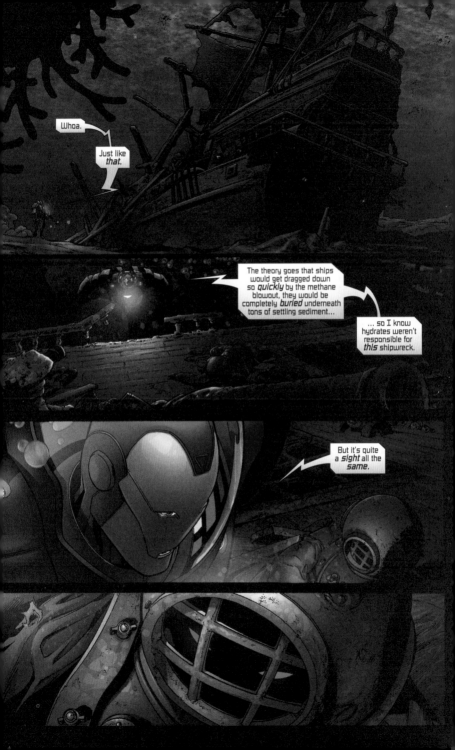

This thing is giving me a headache.

Aye, I'd wager the cranial interface is set to the regular user's brainwave patterns--so your gray matter's gettin' bioelectric feedback.

Tell me quick, then--with the magnetic image resonator--am I any closer to blasting through the lock mechanism?

Almost...

"...maybe two or three more inches.

"And knock off the Long John Silver talk, huh?

"It's not like the Captain's in earshot."

"...before these pirates cause any *permanent* damage with it."

Make yourselves *comfy*, eggheads!

KKKKRRRZZZZZ

I'm turning this *closet* into the Hydro-base *brig!*

No... *dead!*

Hunk of *junk...*

Watch your *mouth.*

The helmet can emit a remote *override signal* to *any* individual armor component.

Still, *your* gut's got no protection against my *cat-o'-nine-tails*--

SNAP!

I like my odds.

Wait! He's up-stairs-- at the *highest* point of the base...

Quite the contrary. I'm **gaining** a body.

An exact **replica** of the one I lost because of **Tony Stark!**

It's only fitting his nanobots **build** it for me.

"It was merciless competition from Stark International that pushed my company--Parks Industries--to the brink of **bankruptcy!**"

"If it weren't for **him,** I never would have cut so many **corners** in my pursuit of physics' **Holy Grail...**

"...a means to convert **matter** to energy!"

It's **his** fault I was transformed into this photo-synthetic **horror**--a **ghost** made out of light!

But soon I'll be **human** again-- able to return to my wife and daughter--

--once I **download** my consciousness into my new **synthetic** body!

I transferred my **brainwave** patterns into the Delphi main-frame in the form of **electrons**--

SSHHHRAAKKK!

You mean **this** main-frame, here?

NOOOOOOO!

The download had already **begun!**

I've got to stop the **data** stream before any particles are lost--

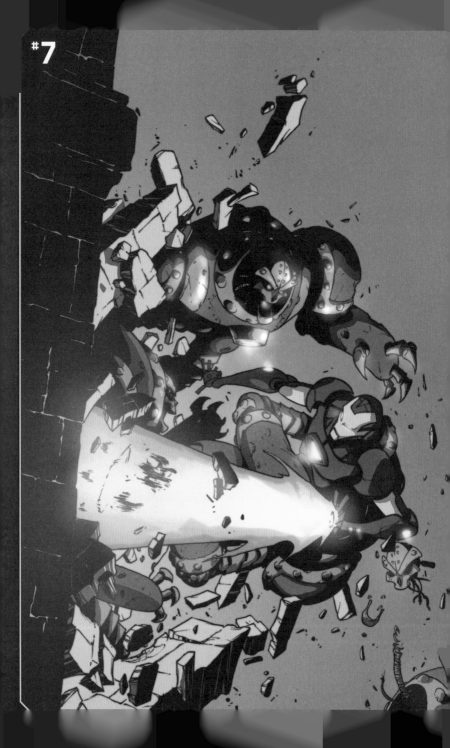

GHOST OF A CHANCE

FRED VAN LENTE — **WRITER**
GRAHAM NOLAN — **PENCILER**

VICTOR OLAZABA — INKER
MARTEGOD GRACIA — COLORIST
DAVE SHARPE — LETTERER
SKOTTIE YOUNG — COVER
RICH GINTER — PRODUCTION
NATHAN COSBY — ASST. EDITOR
MARK PANICCIA — EDITOR
JOE QUESADA — EDITOR IN CHIEF
DAN BUCKLEY — PUBLISHER

BILLIONAIRE INVENTOR TONY STARK BUILT A SUIT OF ARMOR THAT SAVED HIS LIFE. HE NOW FIGHTS AGAINST THE FORCES OF EVIL AS THE INVINCIBLE *IRON MAN!*

In just a few *hours,* my latest set of Iron Man armor will be *complete.*

Shellhead's subterranean togs will allow me to drill deep below Earth's surface-- and withstand the molten heat of the planet's core.

BRRR BRRR BRRR BRRR

Eh? Can't *answer* that--

--not when I'm so close to the *finish line!*

BRRR BRRR BRRR BRRR

THE BALKANS:

Told you he wouldn' pick up!

Tone got bit by the *"inventing bug"* bad, Pepper--that's why he didn't come along on the annual S.I. corporate *retreat* this year.

Renting out a *ski resort* in Central Europe was his *best* idea yet!

That's okay, Rhodey. I just wanted to *thank* him again.

I **can't** let my technology fall into Doom's hands-- but I can't abandon my **friends**, either!

But five hours...Latveria is on the other side of the **world!** Even if I **could** get there in time...

...if I stormed the castle as **Iron Man**, I'd endanger the hostages' lives.

Unless...

It's a **huge risk**...but it's not like I have a lot of **options!**

Of **all** my specialty armors...the **Deep-Sea** armor...the **Outer Space** armor...

The one I haven't had a chance to **try out** yet...

...is my plastic "**Ghost**" Armor!

I designed it for missions requiring the utmost **stealth!**

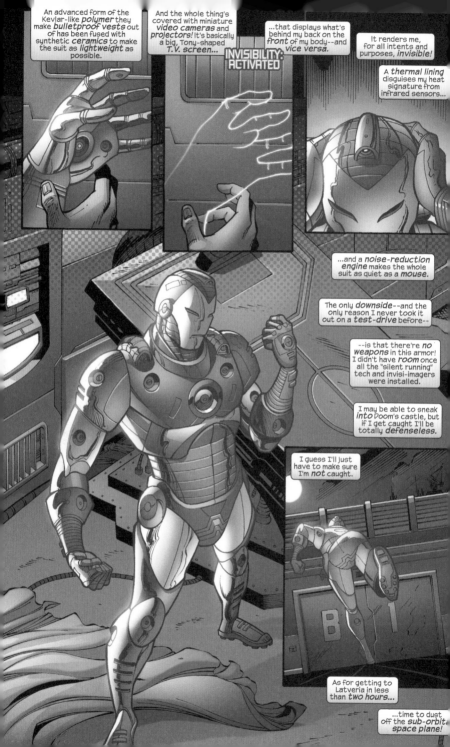

An advanced form of the Kevlar-like *polymer* they make *bulletproof vests* out of has been fused with synthetic *ceramics* to make the suit as *lightweight* as possible.

And the whole thing's covered with miniature *video cameras* and *projectors*! It's basically a big, Tony-shaped *T.V. screen*...

INVISIBILITY: ACTIVATED

...that displays what's behind my back on the *front* of my body--and *vice versa*.

It renders me, for all intents and purposes, *invisible*!

A *thermal lining* disguises my heat signature from infrared sensors...

...and a *noise-reduction engine* makes the whole suit as quiet as a *mouse*.

The only *downside*--and the only reason I never took it out on a *test-drive* before--

--is that there're *no weapons* in this armor! I didn't have *room* once all the "silent running" tech and invisi-imagers were installed.

I may be able to sneak *into* Doom's castle, but if I get caught I'll be totally *defenseless*.

I guess I'll just have to make sure I'm *not* caught.

B 1

As for getting to Latveria in less than *two hours*...

...time to dust off the *sub-orbital space plane*!

This experimental jet shoots *straight up* into outer space at a *kilometer a second*...

...literally *hopping* between continents before dropping back down to its intended destination.

The autopilot will take over from *here*.

Before Doom's flying robots can catch *up* with it--or even *identify* it--the space plane will be *far* outside Latverian airspace.

Without *me*, though.

CLCHINK

And by flicking this *switch* I send the ntest of *electrical currents* through the glider...

...causing it to instantly *self-destruct*, leaving no *traces* for guards to find.

Its special material works on the same principle as magicians' "flash paper."

I've only got *two hours* to find Rhodey, Pepper and the others.

INVISIBILITY: ACTIVATED

Call me *crazy*, but if they're being held in the *dungeons*...

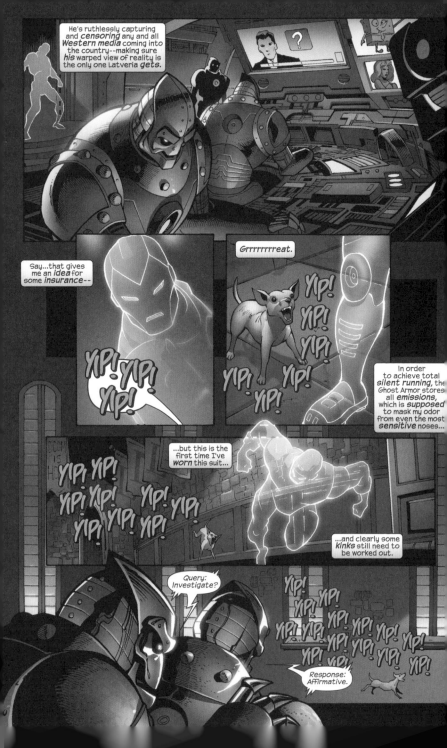

Ohrs 00min

All-rise! Latverian-Supreme-Court-now-in-session!

Chief-Justice-for-Life-the-honorable-**Doctor-Doom**-presiding!

Defendant-**Iron-Man**-is-charged-with-twelve-counts-espionage-one-count-Doombot-destruction-twenty-counts-plotting-the-overthrow-of-the-Republic.

How does the accused plead?

One hundred percent *guilty!*

Does the prisoner have anything to *say* before this court passes judgment?

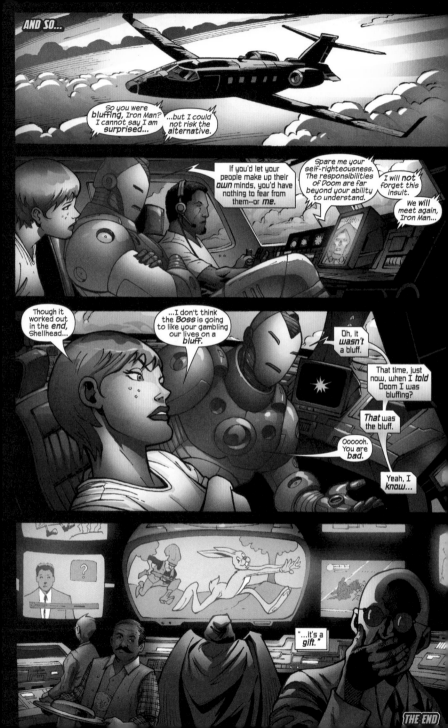

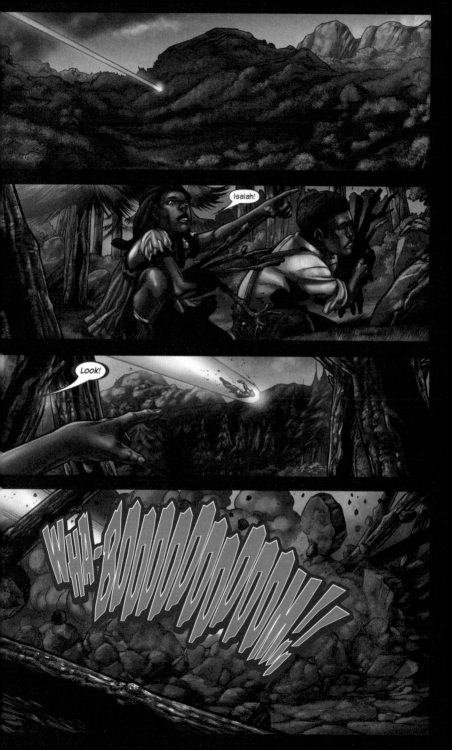

Ma!!

Mr. Hobbes!

Kids? Are you all right?

Did that meteor landing scare you? We were just going to go--

It's not a meteor! It's a man!

It is! I saw his arms and legs and everything!

He could be hurt!

We'd better get out there now!

Hee-YAAHH!!

How... How can he still be alive?

He *is*--it's a *miracle!*

We need to get him to Healer *Yoo* right away!

Hannah, help me get him into the *cart*--

...No.

What?

He's from the *outside.* Bringing him back to town violates the *Principle*--

Hannah...your faithfulness to the Principle is *admirable,* but don't let it curdle into *fanaticism!*

Part of the Principle is *duty* to our fellow human beings!

We *must* use everything--*within* the Principle--to *save* this man.

On *three,* now--

One... two... ≷nnnnnfff!≶

Unnnnhh...

There, there. **Don't** move around too **much,** stranger.

We set your **broken leg** as best we could, but you're not out of the woods just **yet.**

Where am I? Who are--

Our village has **no name.** It's not even on a **map.** And that's the way we **like** it.

We've all... **opted out** of the modern world.

I used to be a **real estate developer.** I was pretty **good** at it, too. Jane **Yoo** here, was head of surgery at **Mt. Sinai.**

But we didn't want the **commercialism** and rampant **violence** of modern America to poison our **families,** so we've chosen to live here, in a **pacifist,** farming society, in the way that made our **ancestors** great.

I don't know how to repay you for what you've done--but--if I could ask **one** more thing--

My people are **worried** about me, I'm sure, and I'd like to **call** to let them know I'm all right-- and so they can come **get** me--

I'm afraid that would be **impossible.** We have no **phones** of any kind--no Internet--no **television.** Technology is strictly **forbidden** here.

And the **thunderstorm** that passed through here last night made the road down the mountain too **rough** for somebody in your condition to go down on **horseback.**

You're stuck **here** until your body does some **healing.**

But don't worry, Mister--

Tony. Just... Tony.

DAYS PASS LAZILY...

That Mr. Hobbes may be *onto* something.

There's no *car horns*--no one yammering on their *cell phone*--people aren't rushing from one meeting or obligation to the *next*.

And...contrary to what every *TV ad* ever *aired* would have you believe...because they have so *little*--they seem perfectly... *happy*.

Almost makes me wonder if *I'm* on the right path...all *semiconductors* and *supersonic jets*.

Aaahh, who am I *kidding*? Mom always said I was born with a *soldering gun* in my hand.

Sometimes you don't *choose* your lifestyle...*it* chooses you!

My stay here *could* be a nice *break* from the "globe-trotting tycoon" grind...

...except "Blue Lightning Woman" could drop out of the sky at any moment to finish what she *started*!

She managed to *fuse* every circuit in my Iron Man armor together--it's *scrap*.

And the fact I'm *crippled* doesn't help much, either.

I need an *equalizer*.

KLANG!

KLANG!

KLANG!

I'm gonna *get* you, Metal Hand!

You're a *bad man!*

Will *not!* I'm gonna *rob banks* and buy a boat!

Nu-*uh!* I'm gonna *beat you up* and lock you in *jail*--

Taneisha! Isaiah! What do you think you're doing?

Violent games are *forbidden* by the Principle!

We're playing "*super hero!*" Mr. *Tony* said it was *okay!*

Did he? Then I got *words* for him. Where *is* Mr. Tony?

He and Luis have been holed up in the *black-smith's* shed for, like, *forever!*

Stark! I'm only gonna say this *once:* You stay *away* from my kids--

Hannah--
wait--

DONG!
DONG!

Town
meeting!
I call a *town*
meeting!

The
newcomer is
building weapons!
Weapons!

In *flagrant*
violation of the
Principle!

I
demand
the town
vote...   ...to
banish
him!

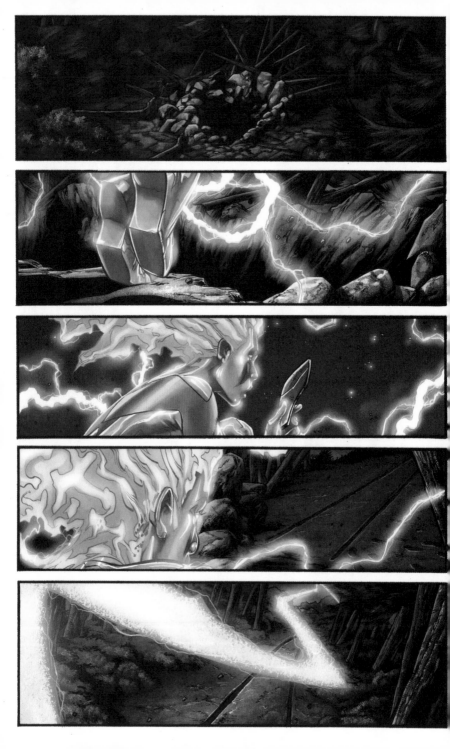

What is that supposed to be?
Steam armor?!
HA HA HA HA HA HA!
You got it.
There's not a single electrical part in it for you to fry.
And a brace to prop up my bum leg...
Big deal. That just means I'll blast you where you stand like a regular person.
SHRAKA-BOOM!
SPLOOOSH!
And--news flash, Shellhead--that water thing doesn't work if I'm braced for it.
You've grounded your-self...with a lightning rod?
Great--you've turned into the mightiest super hero of the nineteenth century!